MATHS FUN FOR COOL KIDS

This is **not** a workbook…but it **is** a book that works

Katie Knapman and Edward Matthews

JUMPING YAK

First published in the UK in 2019 by Jumping Yak

www.jumpingyak.com

ISBN 978-1-9161012-0-3

Printed and bound in the UK by Elanders

About this Book

Would you like to inject more joy into your child's maths?

Does your child need a change from traditional workbooks?

Well, here it is!

This maths puzzle book is full of UK maths curriculum-related activities. The syllabus has been livened up with word problems, cartoons and jokes, making this book a fun activity for any child aged 9 to 12.

Let them delight in decimals, perfect their percentages, size up some shapes and be amazed by simple algebra – it's all included. And rather than being arranged by topic, the puzzles are presented randomly to dip in and out of whenever your child needs a break from more formal study.

Warning! On some pages there is a 'Brain Bender!' stamp. These pages are a little trickier and may require some lateral thinking.

These puzzles show that maths really can be fun!

Words and puzzles by Katie Knapman

After graduating from Oxford University, Katie worked for the BBC and Channel 4, making and presenting leading educational programmes and prime-time shows including *Maths 4 Real*, *Tomorrow's World* and *Countryfile*. Following on from the success of her first book, *Revision Fun for Clever Kids*, she decided to write this book with Edward and Beach. Katie lives in London with her husband and two children.

Puzzles by Edward Matthews

Edward is a maths teacher at Westminster Under School, one of the leading schools in London. He loves numbers, whether in the classroom or the bingo hall. Like many of his students, he is passionate about music and football – he is in a band and follows Manchester United across Europe – and relishes finding ways to incorporate these passions into his lessons.

Drawings by Beach

Beach has three children and two bicycles. For the rest of the time he works as an illustrator and cartoonist.

Contents

Fun Factors............................ 6

What Comes Next?.................... 7

King Henry VIII 8

Digit Fidget........................... 9

Mirror Mirror 10

Pesky Pyramids 11

Number Crunching 12

Super Powers! 14

Divide and Conquer 16

The Bard of Avon................... 17

Mixed Problems..................... 18

Who Am I? 20

Crossword Shapes................. 22

The Great Divide.................... 23

Magic Multiplication 24

Town Planning 25

Polynomial Polygon................ 26

Mental Maths Ladder 28

Countdown!.......................... 29

Gridlock............................... 30

Operation Overlord................. 31

Proportion Problems 32

WYSIWYG* 34

Divide and Conquer Again 36

Lateral Thinking 37

Mysterioso! 38

Shape Up! 39

Algebra................................ 40

More Gridlock........................ 41

Alphabet Soup 42

More Pesky Pyramids 43

More Magic Multiplication 44

Criss Cross 45

I'm Thinking of Two Numbers....46

Maths Investigation................ 48

More Fun Factors.................... 50

Top of the Class..................... 51

Murder in the Cathedral 52

Mental Maths Ladder 2 53

Deadly Decimals.................... 54

A Mean Challenge.................. 55

Crack the Code...................... 56

Additional Algebra 58

Answers............................... 59

Fun Factors

Divide 60 by each number next to it on the eye (working outwards) to practice your mental division.

How quickly can you complete the eye and find all the factor pairs of 60?

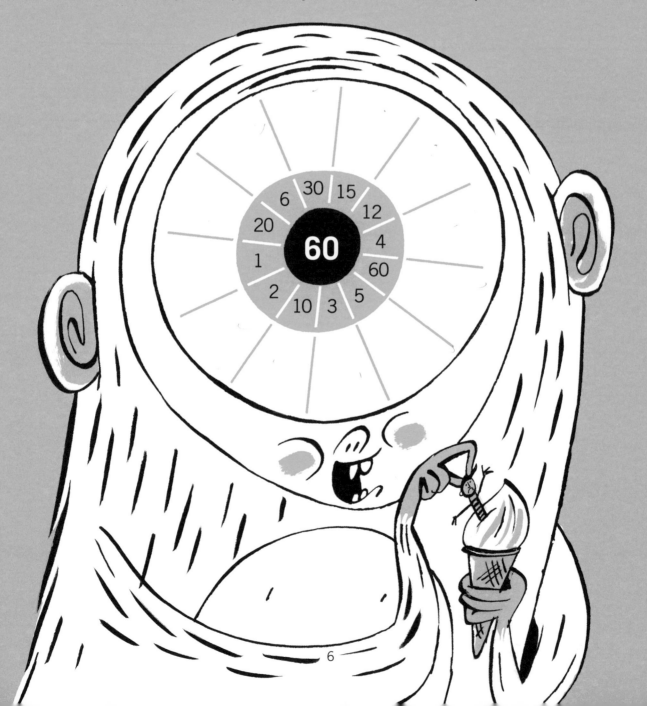

What Comes Next?

Can you work out the next numbers in these sequences?

29	25	21	17	13	9	
10	9.4	8.8	8.2	7.6	7	
3	6	12	24	48	96	
3	6	9	15	24	39	
12	13	16	21	28	37	
4	12	36	108	324	972	
10	6	2	−2	−6	−10	
−21	−17	−13	−9	−5	−1	
1001	931	861	791	721	651	
99	98	97	96	95	94	

7

King Henry VIII

King Henry VIII is best known for marrying six times, beheading two of his wives and for splitting from the Catholic Church.

Use the clues below to work out his date of birth.

(dd)	(mm)	(yyyy)
$(2 \times 4) + (2 \times 5 \times 2)$	$\sqrt{36}$	$3 \times (400 + 45 + 52)$

Digit Fidget

366   16   5   26   15   21   13   12   180   50   125   4

17   3600

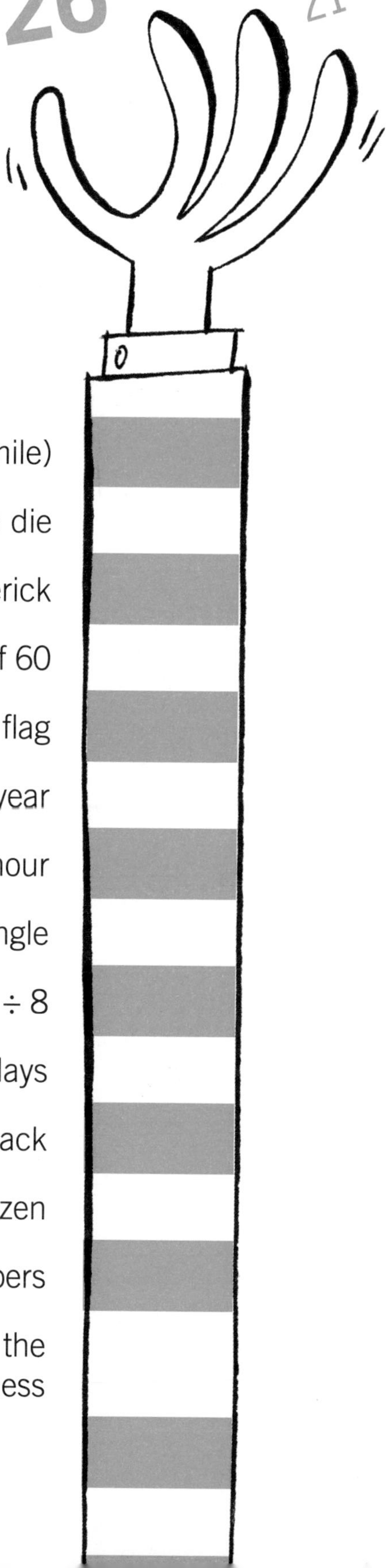

Number of miles in a marathon race (to nearest mile)

Total dots on a die

Lines in a limerick

25% of 60

Number of stars on the US flag

Days in a leap year

Seconds in an hour

Degrees in a triangle

$1000 \div 8$

Number of months with 30 days

Number of cards in each suit in a pack

A dozen

The sum of the first 4 prime numbers

Number of pieces each player has at the start of a game of chess

Mirror Mirror

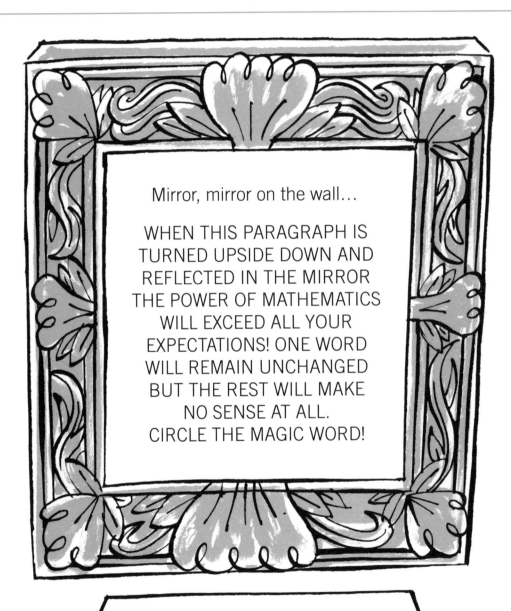

Mirror, mirror on the wall…

WHEN THIS PARAGRAPH IS
TURNED UPSIDE DOWN AND
REFLECTED IN THE MIRROR
THE POWER OF MATHEMATICS
WILL EXCEED ALL YOUR
EXPECTATIONS! ONE WORD
WILL REMAIN UNCHANGED
BUT THE REST WILL MAKE
NO SENSE AT ALL.
CIRCLE THE MAGIC WORD!

There are 9 letters in the alphabet that
work in the same way as the letters in the
magic word, using horizontal lines of symmetry.
Can you work out which ones they are?

10

Pesky Pyramids

These are number pyramids. The number in each block is the sum of the two blocks beneath it. Fill in the empty blocks below.

Number Crunching

Testing Time

Freddie gets 20% on a test with 10 questions, 80% on a test with 20 problems and 90% on a 30-problem test. If the three tests are combined, what is his overall percentage?

Cool in the Pool

Ruby, Oliver and Grace love swimming. Their father Adam wants them to be Olympic champions! Grace can swim 3 times as far as her brother Oliver but only half as far as her sister Ruby who can swim 450 metres. How far can Oliver and Grace swim?

Oliver _____ Grace _____

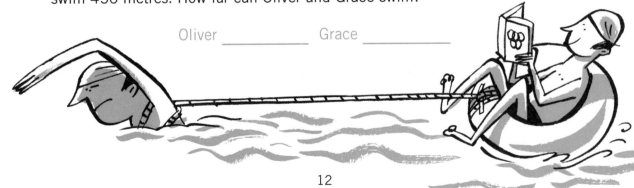

Dividing Sugar

Divide 600g into two parts so that one part is three times that of the other.

_____   _____

Age-old Problem

Jack is 5 years old and Jill is 9.

1) How many years older will Jill be than Jack in 3 years time?   _____

2) How old was Jill when she was twice as old as Jack?   _____

3) How old was Jill when she was three times Jack's age?   _____

Ponder on the Problem

In a village pond, the lilies grew so fast that they doubled the area they were covering every day. After 30 days, the entire pond was covered. After how many days was the pond only half covered?   _____

Super Powers!

The power of a number shows how many of the same number are multiplied together.

For example 2^3 means 'two to the power of three,' or $2 \times 2 \times 2$, which equals 8.

The first ten powers of 2 (the doubling sequence) are shown below:

2 (2^1)	4 (2^2)	8 (2^3)	16 (2^4)	32 (2^5)	64 (2^6)	128 (2^7)	256 (2^8)	512 (2^9)	1024 (2^{10})

These 10 powers can all be matched to the clues below. Work out the answers to the clues and then calculate the powers of 2.

The first one has been done for you.

8 x 8 x 8	512	$= 2 \times 2 \times 2 \times 2 \times 2 \times 2 \times 2 \times 2 \times 2 = 2^9$
The only even prime number		
Other than 1, the lowest number that is a cube and a square		
16^2		
The first number alphabetically and a number which is 1 less than a square number		
The fourth square number		
$1^1 + 2^2 + 3^3 =$		
The only number where the number of letters equals its value		
256 × 4		
640 ÷ 5		

Divide and Conquer

Sometimes, when you need to divide by a number larger than 12, you can make the problem easier by looking for the factors of the number and then breaking the problem down into stages.

So, for example, if dividing by 35, find a factor pair – in this example 5 and 7. First divide by 5 and then divide your answer by 7.

Divide each of the numbers below by 35 and then convert your answer to a letter (1=A, 2=B etc). Two columns have been filled in for you to get you started.

350	735	455	560	315	490	245		875	35	385
		13			14					
		M			N					

A	B	C	D	E	F	G	H	I	J	K	L	M
1	2	3	4	5	6	7	8	9	10	11	12	13

N	O	P	Q	R	S	T	U	V	W	X	Y	Z
14	15	16	17	18	19	20	21	22	23	24	25	26

The Bard of Avon

Shakespeare was an English poet, playwright and actor from Stratford-upon-Avon, and he is widely regarded as the greatest writer in the English language.

Use the clues below to work out his supposed date of birth.

(dd)	(mm)	(yyyy)
The day is a two-digit prime number. The two digits are consecutive numbers	The number of days in this month is a multiple of the number of letters in the month's name	2 × (625 + 125 + 25 + 5 + 2)

Mixed Problems

On Your Marks

There are 20 exercise books on the table in 4 piles. The first pile has 3 fewer than the second pile. The second pile has 2 more than the third pile. The fourth pile has twice as many as the second pile. How many books are in each pile?

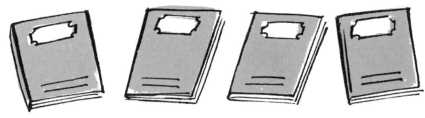

Father and Son

John told his son that he was twice as old as his son is now, on the day that he was born. He then said, "In 14 years time, you will be the age I was when you were born." How old are they now?

_____   _____

Money in the Bank

Albert has £15 more than Ross in his piggy bank. Together they have £43. How much money does each man have?

Albert   Ross

Quick Conversion

Complete the missing boxes in the table below, writing the fractions in their lowest terms.

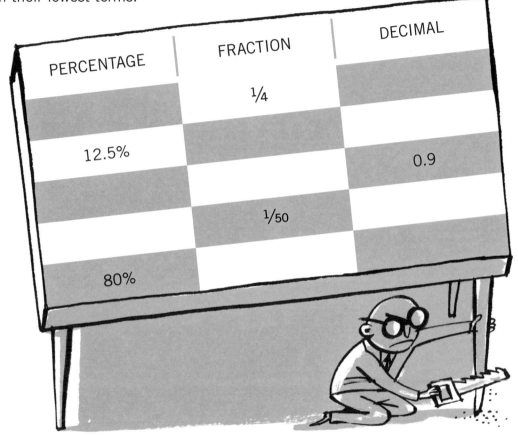

PERCENTAGE	FRACTION	DECIMAL
	¼	
12.5%		0.9
	1/50	
80%		

Zoolemma

221 new creatures – birds, monkeys and snakes – are being delivered to a zoo. The number of tropical birds and snakes is 149 and the number of tropical birds and monkeys together is 178. How many birds, snakes and monkeys are being delivered?

19

Who Am I?

Can you work out each player's shirt number?

I am a square number,
an odd number
between 20 and 50,
and 7 is one of my factors.

I am between 50 and 90.
I am even.
I am a multiple of 8
and have 24 as one of my factors.

I am even.
I am under 79.
I am a multiple of 10
and have 3, 4 and 5 as factors.

I am prime. I am under 40.
I have two digits and the sum of
these is odd.
If you double me and subtract 9
you are left with a square number.

I am a three-figure number. I am even.
My digits descend consecutively.
I have 4 and 6 as factors.
The sum of my digits is 9.

Crossword Shapes

Across

2) A 3-D rectangle (6)
3) The only 3-D shape with one face (6)
4) Rubik's _____ (4)
5) A 12-sided shape (9)
6) A prism with 5 faces (10, 5)

Down

1) Another name for a triangular pyramid (11)
2) The shape of a telescope (8)
4) Ice cream is served in this (4)

You're pointless!

The Great Divide

Arrange the digits from 1 to 6 on the circles to make the statement correct. The 3 has been done for you.

Magic Multiplication

Complete this grid as fast as you can!

×	12	2	4	5	3	11	9	7	10	6	8	1	×
6													6
11													11
8													8
3													3
7													7
10													10
12													12
5													5
2													2
9													9
4													4
1													1
×	12	2	4	5	3	11	9	7	10	6	8	1	×

Time to complete this grid:

_____

Town Planning

From the clues given, correctly label the towns A to F and answer the questions.

Clues:

— Town F is northeast of town B and north of town E
— Town C is south of town E and west of town D

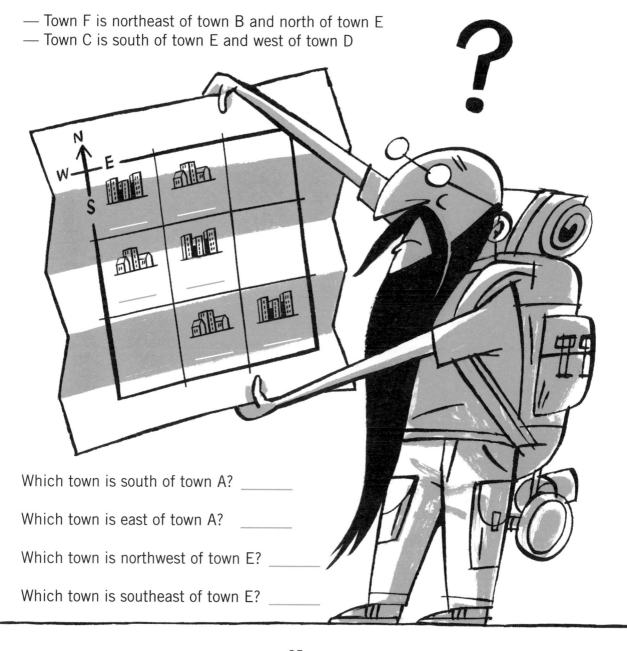

Which town is south of town A? _____

Which town is east of town A? _____

Which town is northwest of town E? _____

Which town is southeast of town E? _____

Polynomial Polygon

Complete this table of square numbers to help you answer the questions opposite (the diagrams are not to scale).

1 × 1	2 × 2	3 × 3	4 × 4	5 × 5	6 × 6	7 × 7	8 × 8	9 × 9	10 × 10	11 × 11	12 × 12

1) The area of this right-angled triangle is $32\,\text{cm}^2$. The lengths of the two perpendicular sides are square numbers. Mark these on the diagram.

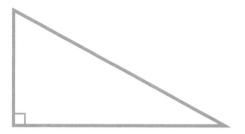

2) The three angles in this scalene triangle are all square numbers. Mark these on the diagram.

3) The four angles in this trapezium are all square numbers. Mark these on the diagram.

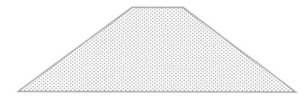

4) A square has an area of $81\ \text{cm}^2$. What is its perimeter?

5) A square has a perimeter of 40 cm. What is its area?

6) What has dimensions of 210 mm by 297 mm?

Mental Maths Ladder

Calculate the answers to the questions and work your way down the ladder putting each answer in the space below. When you have completed the page, put the numbers into your calculator and turn it upside down to find the name of a famous book.

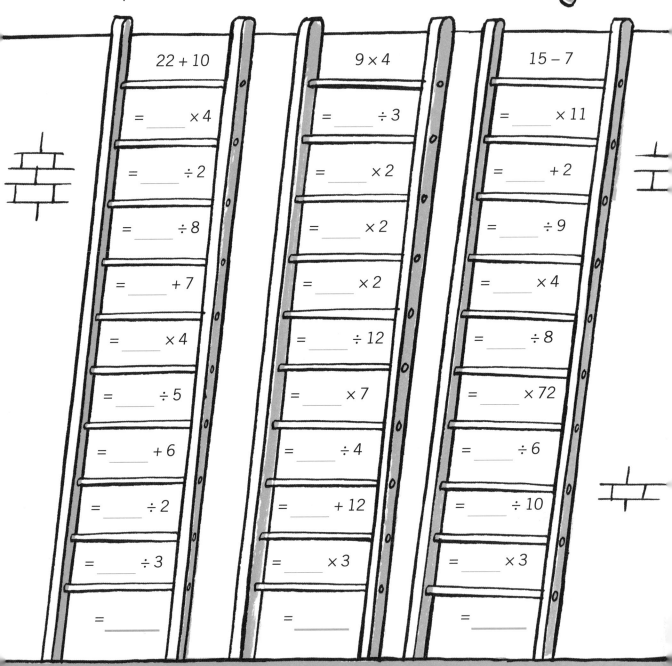

Ladder 1

22 + 10

= _____ × 4

= _____ ÷ 2

= _____ ÷ 8

= _____ + 7

= _____ × 4

= _____ ÷ 5

= _____ + 6

= _____ ÷ 2

= _____ ÷ 3

= _____

Ladder 2

9 × 4

= _____ ÷ 3

= _____ × 2

= _____ × 2

= _____ × 2

= _____ ÷ 12

= _____ × 7

= _____ ÷ 4

= _____ + 12

= _____ × 3

= _____

Ladder 3

15 − 7

= _____ × 11

= _____ + 2

= _____ ÷ 9

= _____ × 4

= _____ ÷ 8

= _____ × 72

= _____ ÷ 6

= _____ ÷ 10

= _____ × 3

= _____

Countdown!

Number the following 11–20.

Number of holes on a golf course

James Bond × 2

XVII

Labours of Hercules

Number of minutes in a quarter of an hour

Number of ounces in a pound

The prime number that comes after 17

Unlucky for some

The First World War ended on this day in this month

A game where you ask this number of questions
(the answers can only be *yes* or *no*)

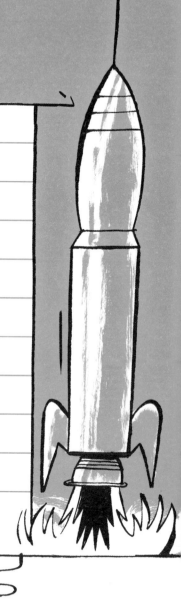

click

Gridlock

Using algebra and common sense, work out the value of the letters in each grid. Can you find the value of the question marks?

$$b + b + b + b = 24$$
$$4b = 24$$
$$b = 6$$

a	d	c	c	
c	b	c	d	22
a	d	a	a	
b	b	b	b	24
16	28	?		

a =   b =   c =

d =   ? =

e	h	f	g	?
e	e	e	e	16
f	h	f	g	12
h	h	e	g	
	13		19	

e =   f =   g =

h =   ? =

30

Operation Overlord

The D-Day landings, also known as Operation Overlord, took place towards the end of the Second World War. This was the date when thousands of allied troops landed on the beaches of Normandy in Northern France at the start of the battle to liberate mainland Europe from Nazi occupation.

Use the clues below to work out what the date was.

(dd)	(mm)	(yyyy)
The third triangular number	Number of sides on a hexagon	$(432 \times 3) + (324 \times 2)$

Proportion Problems

Smooth Operators

34% of families in school own a smoothie maker. There are 200 families – how many can make smoothies?

Le Français

Jenny got 28 out of 40 in a French test. What was her mark as a percentage?

Comedy Cash

Laurel and Hardy are given £77 in the ratio 8:3.

How much money does Hardy get?

Cross Country

The journey from Oxford to Cambridge is 84 miles. If Mr Blobby has driven ⅙ of the way to Cambridge, how far does he still have to go?

Bed and Breakfast

A man looks at two hotels to stay in with his family on holiday. The first costs £1,200 and the second is £1,560. How much more expensive in percentage terms is the second hotel than the first?

Dressing Down

In an end-of-season sale, everything is 30% off. How much is a dress that cost £45 originally, and if you have £8.50 change, how much money did you pay with?

Parking Lot

There are 150 cars in a car park. 18% are red, 26% are white, 8% are yellow and 14% are green. How many blue cars are there if the remaining cars are blue?

WYSIWYG*

Identify the pictures below and then find the words in the word search grid.

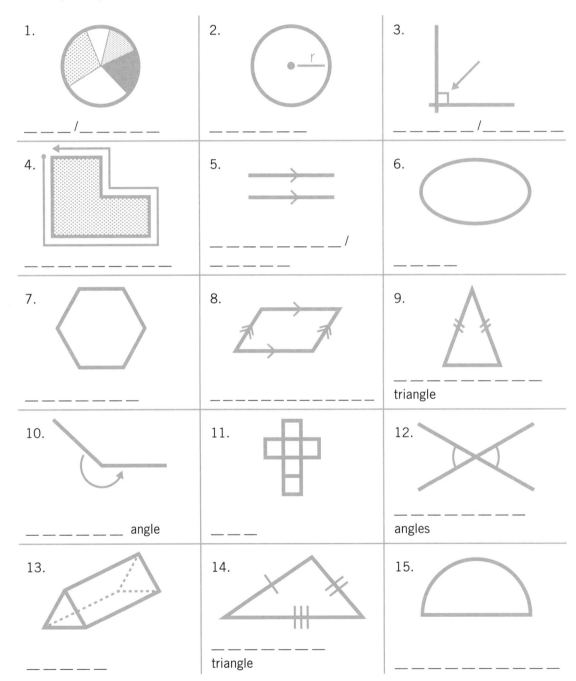

1.

_ _ _ / _ _ _ _ _

2.

_ _ _ _ _ _

3.

_ _ _ _ _ / _ _ _ _ _

4.

_ _ _ _ _ _ _ _ _

5.

_ _ _ _ _ _ _ _ _ _ /

6.

_ _ _ _

7.

_ _ _ _ _ _ _

8.

_ _ _ _ _ _ _ _ _ _ _ _ _

9.

_ _ _ _ _ _ _ _ _
triangle

10.

_ _ _ _ _ _ _ angle

11.

_ _ _

12.

_ _ _ _ _ _ _ _
angles

13.

_ _ _ _ _

14.

_ _ _ _ _ _ _
triangle

15.

_ _ _ _ _ _ _ _ _

34

```
M D R X Z D G O P P O S I T E
T I V R N S S C Z S W W V W V
P T U Q I R C C K E T N U S W
A R M C U S I A I O E Z M L G
R A Z T X W O G L Z L X X P U
A D P H Z I L S H E A T V N K
L I S E O V A L C T N I W W O
L U P X R W D G B E A E X U B
E S V A T I Y L Y K L N R Z P
L O S G R D M N O M X E G O S
L Z B O K A T E G K B U S L T
I D U N J Z L Y T R X D O P E
N R C A A A W L D E P Z M J P
E H P P H U M A E S R R B I T
S S E M I C I R C L E Y I A K
A N T S Z P L R S P O M J S H
J X N Y L C Q B C K K G C J M
B D E R E F L E X M R J R E O
K A T O F E U N K P R R F A O
X Q P I E C H A R T B A J V M
```

35

Divide and Conquer Again

WHY CAN WEARING GLASSES HELP PUPILS IN A MATHS CLASS?

Find the answer to the question by dividing each of the numbers below by 27.

If, like me, you don't know your 27-times table, you can just divide by the factors 3 and then 9.

Convert your answer to a letter using the key at the bottom of the page.

Two columns have been filled in for you to get you started.

243	540		243	351	432	486	405	594	135	513
	20									
	T									

108	243	594	243	513	243	405	378
							14
							N

A	B	C	D	E	F	G	H	I	J	K	L	M
1	2	3	4	5	6	7	8	9	10	11	12	13

N	O	P	Q	R	S	T	U	V	W	X	Y	Z
14	15	16	17	18	19	20	21	22	23	24	25	26

Lateral Thinking

Can you work out the next letters in these sequences?*

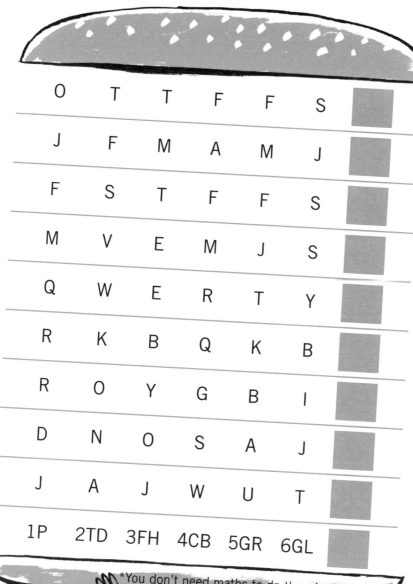

O	T	T	F	F	S	
J	F	M	A	M	J	
F	S	T	F	F	S	
M	V	E	M	J	S	
Q	W	E	R	T	Y	
R	K	B	Q	K	B	
R	O	Y	G	B	I	
D	N	O	S	A	J	
J	A	J	W	U	T	
1P	2TD	3FH	4CB	5GR	6GL	

*You don't need maths to do these!

Mysterioso!

Find two numbers whose product is 63 and whose sum is 16.
$x + y = 16$ and $xy = 63$

Find two numbers whose product is 65 and whose difference is 8.
$x - y = 8$ and $xy = 65$

The sum of four numbers is 30. When the four numbers are arranged in order, smallest first, each number is twice the number before it. Find the four numbers.

Who am I? The product of my digits is 7 and the sum of my digits is 8.

 or

Matthew, his little brother Mark, their father Luke and their grandfather John have ages that are different cube numbers. John is not yet 100. How old was John when Matthew was born?

What number when squared is equal to the sum of the first 7 odd numbers?

Shape Up!

How well do you know your shapes?

Identify the shapes and fill in the blanks in the grid. When you have named all the shapes, the vertical word will spell the name of a famous mathematician.

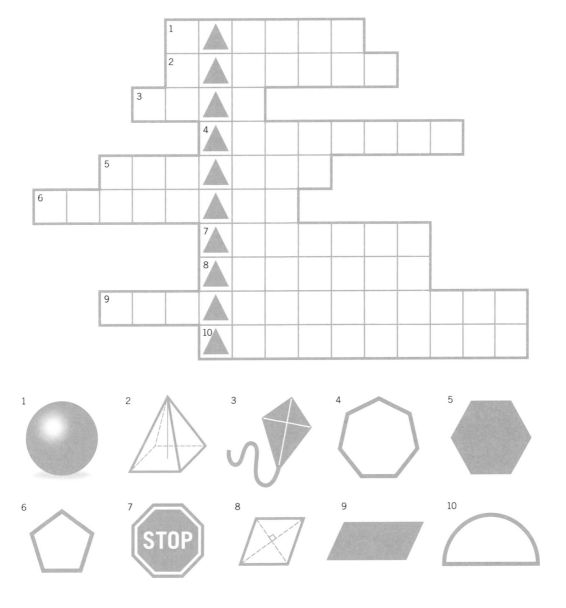

Algebra

Amaze your friends with your powers of deduction!

Think of any positive number, multiply by 5, add 1, double what you have, take away 2 and divide by the number you first thought of. What answer do you get?

_____

Number Run

The sum of 5 consecutive numbers is 230. What is the smallest of these 5 numbers?

_____

Play It Again Sam

In 8 years from now, Sam will be three times as old as he was 12 years ago. What is his age now?

_____

Clever Claude

Claude thinks of a number. He then multiplies it by 3, subtracts 7, multiplies by 2 then adds 22. He finds that the number he ends up with is 8 times his original number. What was his original number?

_____

Find De ABC

Find the values of A,B,C,D and E when

$2A + B = 100$ A_____

$B = 2A$ B_____

$C + 2D = B$ C_____

$A = D + E$ D_____

$4E = D$ E_____

Why do you always have to be so negative?!

40

More Gridlock

Using algebra and common sense, work out what numbers the letters stand for, and in turn, the question marks.

a	b	d	c	?
d	b	d	c	
a	d	d	a	24
c	a	d	d	
20	16	28		

a =   b =   c =

d =   ? =

e	h	g	h	22
e	e	e	e	20
f	g	h	g	
f	e	f	h	20
18		?		

e =   f =   g =

h =   ? =

Alphabet Soup

Can you work out the next letters in these sequences?

This will help you:

A B C D E F G H I J K L M N O P Q R S T U V W X Y Z

Z	Y	X	W	V	U	
A	C	E	G	I	K	
A	Z	B	Y	C	X	
C	F	I	L	O	R	
A	B	D	G	K	P	
Z	T	O	K	H	F	
A	P	C	R	E	T	
ZA	YB	XC	WD	VE	UF	
AB	BD	CF	DH	EJ	FL	
WX	SA	OD	KG	GJ	CM	

If you leave Alphabet Soup on the stove and go out, it could spell 'DISASTER!'

42

More Pesky Pyramids

The number in each block is the sum of the two blocks beneath it. Fill in the empty blocks below.

And finally, by placing
the numbers 1 to 5
in the bottom row of this pyramid,
what is the largest possible number
in the top block?

More Magic Multiplication

This is the same grid as the one on page 24. Can you beat your time?

×	12	2	4	5	3	11	9	7	10	6	8	1	×
6													6
11													11
8													8
3													3
7													7
10													10
12													12
5													5
2													2
9													9
4													4
1													1
×	12	2	4	5	3	11	9	7	10	6	8	1	×

Time to complete this grid:

_____

Criss Cross

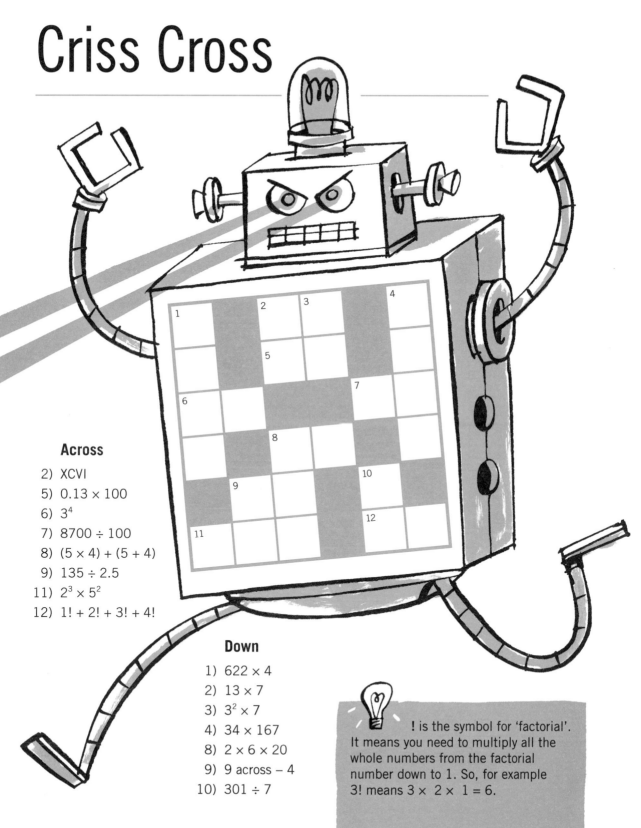

Across

2) XCVI
5) 0.13×100
6) 3^4
7) $8700 \div 100$
8) $(5 \times 4) + (5 + 4)$
9) $135 \div 2.5$
11) $2^3 \times 5^2$
12) $1! + 2! + 3! + 4!$

Down

1) 622×4
2) 13×7
3) $3^2 \times 7$
4) 34×167
8) $2 \times 6 \times 20$
9) 9 across − 4
10) $301 \div 7$

! is the symbol for 'factorial'. It means you need to multiply all the whole numbers from the factorial number down to 1. So, for example 3! means $3 \times 2 \times 1 = 6$.

45

I'm Thinking of Two Numbers

Sum!
The result of adding two or more numbers

Difference!
The result of subtracting one number from another

Product!
The result of multiplying two or more numbers

Quotient!
The result obtained by dividing one number by another

Their sum is 32 and their difference is 12

Their sum is 100 and their difference is 10

Their sum is 20 and their difference is 2

Their sum is 0 and their difference is 2

Their sum is 22 and their product is 120

Their sum is 55 and their quotient is 4

Their difference is 3 and their product is 40

Their difference is 35 and their quotient is 6

Their product is 36 and their quotient is 4

Their sum is 2, their difference is 0,
their product is 1, their quotient is 1

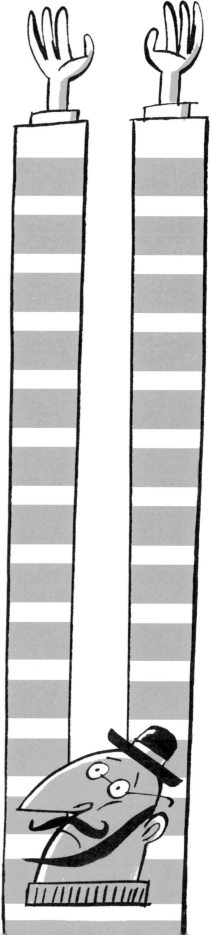

STICK 'EM UP!

Maths Investigation

A **prime number** is a number that can only be divided by itself and 1. The number 1 is not thought of as a prime number. 2 and 3 are the first two prime numbers.

A **square number** is the result of multiplying a number by itself. 1, 4 and 9 are the first three square numbers because 1 x 1 = 1, 2 x 2 = 4 and 3 x 3 = 9.

A **triangular number** is a number that can make a triangular dot pattern. 1, 3, and 6 are the first three triangular numbers.

A **cube number** is the result of multiplying a number by itself, and then itself again. 1, 8 and 27 are the first three cube numbers because 1 x 1 x 1 = 1, 2 x 2 x 2 = 8 and 3 x 3 x 3 = 27.

Complete the grid below with the numbers that come next and then answer the questions at the bottom of the page.

PRIMES	2	3								
SQUARE	1	4								
TRIANGULAR	1	3	6							
CUBES	1	8								

Can you think of three consecutive numbers that fit these categories:

Prime, cube, square?

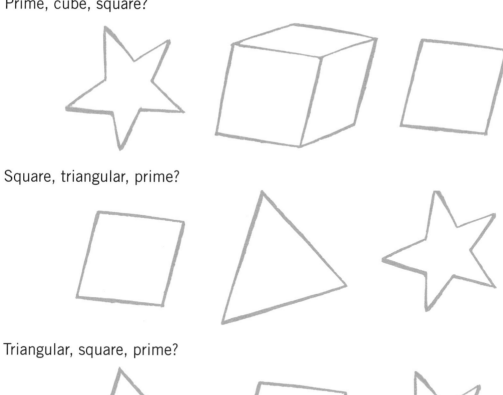

Square, triangular, prime?

Triangular, square, prime?

49

More Fun Factors

Divide 48 by each number next to it on the pizza slice (working outwards) to practice your mental division.

How quickly can you complete the pizza and find all the factor pairs of 48?

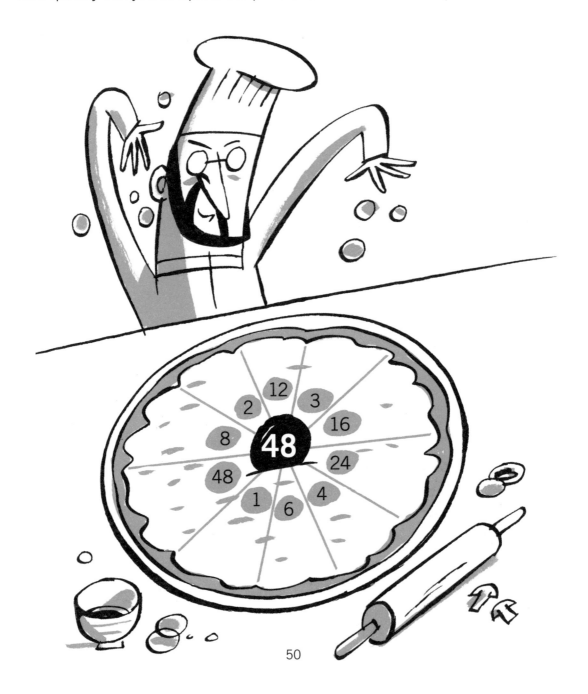

Top of the Class

In a recent maths test, the students were marked out of 120.
Convert their marks into percentages.

Name	Mark out of 120	Percentage %
Harry	54	
Ryan	102	
Mark	6	
Logan	108	
Oliver	114	
Isla	72	
Lily	84	
Heidi	120	
Emily	30	
Freya	48	

Hint:

To find the percentage, divide the mark by 120 and multiply by 100.
So, if a student scores 114 their percentage is:

$$\frac{114}{120} \times 100 = 95\%$$

Murder in the Cathedral

Thomas Becket was Archbishop of Canterbury in Henry II's reign. He is famous for being brutally murdered in Canterbury Cathedral following a disagreement with Henry II about the power of the church and the power of the king.
Use the clues below to find the date he was murdered.

(dd)	(mm)	(yyyy)
The tenth prime number	$3^2 + 2^2 - 1^2$	3×390

Mental Maths Ladder 2

Calculate the answers to the questions and work your way down the ladder putting each answer in the space below. When you have completed the page, put the numbers into your calculator and turn it upside down to find the name of one of the girls visiting the zoo.

ZOO

Ladder 1

30 – 4

= _____ ÷ 13

= _____ × 4

= _____ × 3

= _____ – 7

= _____ – 11

= _____ × 5

= _____ ÷ 10

= _____ + 2

= _____ × 7

= _____

Ladder 2

100 ÷ 10

= _____ – 7

= _____ × 3

= _____ + 9

= _____ × 3

= _____ ÷ 6

= _____ × 2

= _____ – 13

= _____ × 4

= _____ ÷ 2

= _____

Ladder 3

144 ÷ 12

= _____ × 5

= _____ ÷ 6

= _____ × 12

= _____ – 31

= _____ – 40

= _____ ÷ 7

= _____ + 10

= _____ × 3

= _____ + 22

= _____

Deadly Decimals

Complete this grid as fast as you can!

×	1.2	0.2	0.4	0.5	0.3	1.5	0.9	0.7	0.1	0.6	0.8	1.0	×
6													6
11													11
8													8
3													3
7													7
10													10
12													12
5													5
2													2
9													9
4													4
1													1
×	1.2	0.2	0.4	0.5	0.3	1.5	0.9	0.7	0.1	0.6	0.8	1.0	×

Time to complete this grid: _____

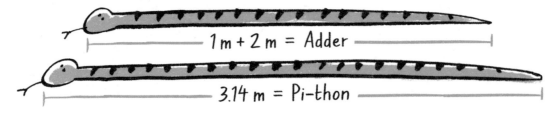

1 m + 2 m = Adder

3.14 m = Pi-thon

A Mean Challenge

Marmaduke the mathematical mutt has set five fiendishly tricky problems involving averages. He has kindly answered the final question for you.

Enter four whole numbers which have a mean, mode, median and range of four

Enter five whole numbers which have a mean, mode, median and range of five

Enter six whole numbers which have a mean, mode, median, mode and range of six

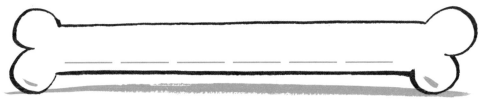

Enter eight whole numbers which have a mean, mode, median and range of eight

Enter ten whole numbers which have a mean, mode, median and range of ten

Crack the Code

We use emojis when writing text messages and emails. They are a modern way of representing words and thoughts using images.

A rebus is a type of puzzle that has been popular since the beginning of time. In these puzzles, a word or part of a word is represented by a picture, letters or numbers. For example:

 = To be or not to be

Below is a rebus for you to solve...

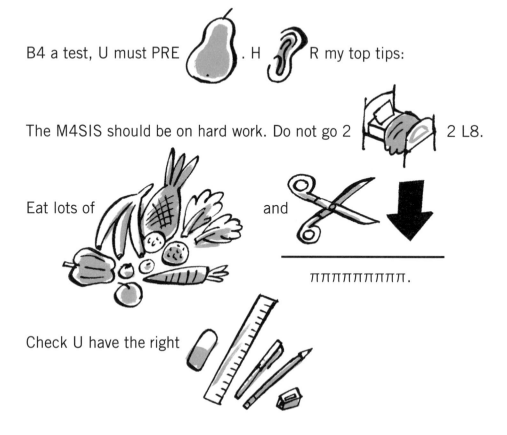

B4 a test, U must PRE ⌇ . H ⌇ R my top tips:

The M4SIS should be on hard work. Do not go 2 ⌇ 2 L8.

Eat lots of ⌇ and ⌇ / ππππππππ.

Check U have the right ⌇

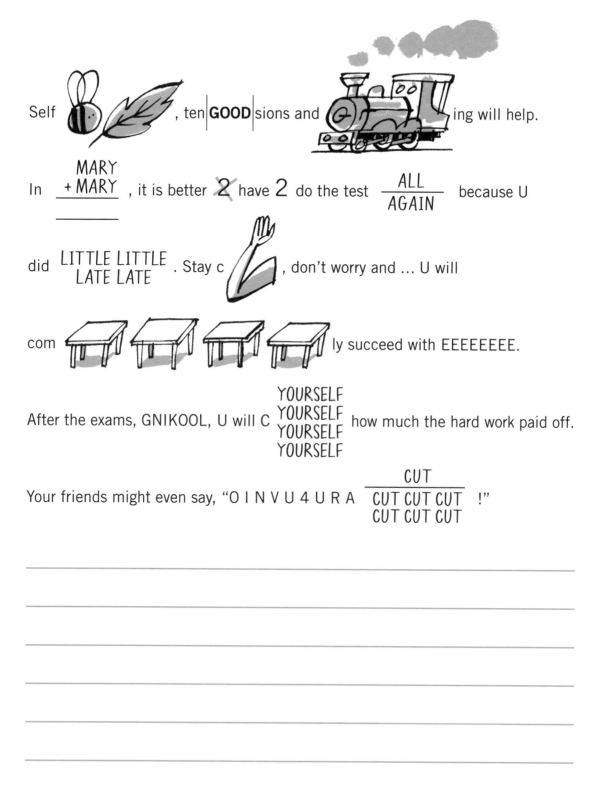

Self <bee><leaf>, ten|**GOOD**|sions and <train> ing will help.

In MARY
    + MARY , it is better 2̶ have 2 do the test ALL
    ‾‾‾‾‾‾   ‾‾‾‾‾
                                                 AGAIN because U

did LITTLE LITTLE . Stay c <arm>, don't worry and … U will
     LATE LATE

com <table><table><table><table> ly succeed with EEEEEEEE.

                              YOURSELF
After the exams, GNIKOOL, U will C YOURSELF how much the hard work paid off.
                              YOURSELF
                              YOURSELF

                                        CUT
                                       ‾‾‾‾‾‾‾‾‾‾‾
Your friends might even say, "O I N V U 4 U R A CUT CUT CUT !"
                                       CUT CUT CUT

Additional Algebra

Winter Warmer

There are 38 boys in the playground. 20 are wearing scarves. 15 are wearing scarves and hats. If 12 boys are not wearing a hat or a scarf, how many boys are wearing a hat without a scarf?

_____

The Bright Side of the Road

The houses on Goa Way are odd on one side of the street and even on the other. The house numbers of 5 neighbouring houses add up to 65. What are those house numbers?

_____ _____ _____ _____ _____

Age-old Problem

I am twice the age of each of my twin sons, Harry and Gary.
Our three ages have a total of 76. How old is Harry?

_____

Party Time

There are five presents for the birthday girl wrapped in different colours.

The red and the purple presents together cost £41
The purple and the blue presents together cost £18
The blue and the yellow presents together cost £26
The yellow and green presents together cost £38
The green and the red presents together cost £47

What is the total cost of all five presents? _____

Answers

Fun Factors (p. 6)
The factor pairs of 60 are:
1 and 60, 2 and 30, 3 and 20, 4 and 15, 5 and 12, 6 and 10.

What Comes Next? (p. 7)
5 (−4), 6.4 (−0.6), 192 (×2),
63 (+previous number),
48 (+next odd number),
2916 (×3 previous number),
−14 (−4), 3 (+4), 581 (−70), 93 (−1)

King Henry VIII (p. 8)
28 / 6 / 1491

Digit Fidget (p. 9)
26 miles, 21 dots, 5 lines, 15, 50 stars, 366 days, 3600 seconds, 180 degrees, 125, 4 months, 13 cards, 12, 17, 16 pieces.

Mirror Mirror (p. 10)
EXCEED (this word has a horizontal line of symmetry). The letters you could use are B C D E H I K O X

Number Crunching (p. 12)
Testing Time: 75%
Cool in the Pool: Oliver 75 m, Grace 225 m
Dividing Sugar: 450 g and 150 g
Age-old Problem: 4, 8 and 6
Ponder on the Problem: 29 days

Super Powers! (p. 14)
512 (2^9); 2 (2^1); 64 (2^6); 256 (2^8); 8 (2^3); 16 (2^4); 32 (2^5); 4 (2^2); 1024 (2^{10}); 128 (2^7)

Divide and Conquer (p. 16)

350	735	455	560	315	490	245
10	21	13	16	9	14	7
J	U	M	P	I	N	G

875	35	385
25	1	11
Y	A	K

The Bard of Avon (p. 17)
23 / 4 / 1564

Pesky Pyramids (p. 11)

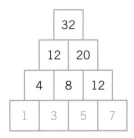
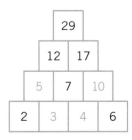
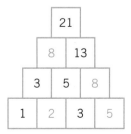

Mixed Problems (p. 18)

On Your Marks – pile 1 = 2 books,
pile 2 = 5 books, pile 3 = 3 books,
pile 4 = 10 books
Father and Son – 42 and 14
Money in the Bank – Albert has £29
and Ross has £14
Quick conversion

Percentage	Fraction	Decimal
25%	1/4	0.25
12.5%	1/8	0.125
90%	9/10	0.9
2%	1/50	0.02
80%	4/5	0.8

Zoolemma – 106 birds, 72 monkeys
and 43 snakes

Who Am I? (p. 20)

Squárez 49, Evens 72, Tenz 60,
Prima 29, Descendiño 432

Crossword Shapes (p. 22)

Across: 2) cuboid, 3) sphere, 4) cube,
5) dodecagon, 6) triangular prism
Down: 1) tetrahedron, 2) cylinder, 4) cone

The Great Divide (p. 23)

$162 \div 54 = 3$

Magic Multiplication (p. 24)

See table on p. 63

Town Planning (p. 25)

B, F, A and D

Polynomial Polygon (p. 26)

1) Base 16 cm, height 4 cm or base
64 cm, height 1 cm
2) 16°, 64° and 100°
3) 36°, 36°, 144°, 144°
4) 36 cm / 5) 100 cm^2 / 6) A4 paper

Mental Maths Ladder (p. 28)

Ladder 1: 32, 128, 64, 8, 15, 60, 12,
18, 9 — Final answer 3
Ladder 2: 36, 12, 24, 48, 96, 8, 56,
14, 26 — Final answer 78
Ladder 3: 8, 88, 90, 10, 40, 5, 360,
60, 6 — Final answer 18
3, 78 and 18 = BIBLE

Countdown! (p. 29)

20 = game where you ask this number of
questions (answers can only be yes or no)
19 = the prime number that follows 17
18 = holes on a golf course; 17 = XVII;
16 = ounces in a pound; 15 = minutes in
quarter of an hour; 14 = James Bond x 2;
13 = unlucky for some; 12 = labours of
Hercules; 11 = The First World War ended
on this day, in this month

Gridlock (p. 30)

a = 3, b = 6, c = 4, d = 8, ? = 17
e = 4, f = 2, g = 5, h = 3, ? = 14

Operation Overlord (p. 31)

6 / 6 / 1944

Proportion Problems (p. 32)

Smooth Operator – 68 families
Le Français – 70%
Comedy Cash – Hardy gets £21
Cross Country – 70 miles
Bed and Breakfast – 30% more
Dressing Down – Dress £31.50, paid £40
Parking Lot – 51 cars are blue

WYSIWYG* (p. 34)

1) pie chart, 2) radius, 3) right angle,
4) perimeter, 5) parallel lines, 6) oval,
7) hexagon, 8) parallelogram, 9) isosceles,
10) reflex, 11) net, 12) opposite,
13) prism, 14) scalene, 15) semicircle

Divide and Conquer Again (p. 36)

243	540
9	20
I	T

243	351	432	486	405	594	135	513
9	13	16	18	15	22	5	19
I	M	P	R	O	V	E	S

108	243	594	243	513	243	405	378
4	9	22	9	19	9	15	14
D	I	V	I	S	I	O	N

Lateral Thinking (p. 37)

S (Seven); J (July); S (Seventh);
U (Uranus); U (Letters on the top row of a UK keyboard); K (Knight – chess board at start of play); V (Violet – rainbow colours); J (June – months backwards);
H (Hill – Jack and Jill went up it);
7SS (Seven swans a-swimming, from the 12 Days of Christmas).

Mysterioso! (p. 38)

7 and 9
5 and 13
2, 4, 8, 16
71 or 17
Matthew 8; Mark 1; Luke 27; John 64; John was 56 when Matthew was born
7 – square root of: $1+3+5+7+9+11+13$

Shape Up! (p. 39)

Sphere, pyramid, kite, heptagon, hexagon, pentagon, octagon, rhombus, parallelogram, semicircle.
The mathematician is **Pythagoras**, famous for his right-angled triangle theorem.

Algebra (p. 40)

Amaze your friends! 10 / Number Run: 44
Play it again Sam: 22 / Clever Claude: 4
ABC: A = 25, B = 50, C = 10, D = 20, E = 5

More Gridlock (p. 41)

a = 5, b = 2, c = 3, d = 7, ? = 17
e = 5, f = 4, g = 3, h = 7, ? = 19

Alphabet Soup (p. 42)

T, M, D, U, V, E, G, TG, GN, YP

More Pesky Pyramids (p. 43)

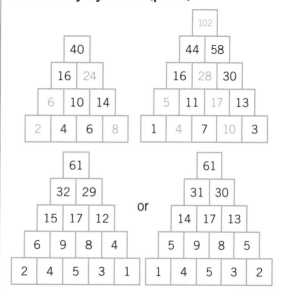

More Magic Multiplication (p. 44)

See table on p. 63

Criss Cross (p. 45)

Across: 2) 96, 5) 13, 6) 81, 7) 87, 8) 29, 9) 54, 11) 200, 12) 33.
Down: 1) 2488, 2) 91, 3) 63, 4) 5678, 8) 240, 9) 50, 10) 43

I'm Thinking of Two Numbers (p. 46)

10 and 22, 45 and 55, 9 and 11,
−1 and 1, 10 and 12, 11 and 44,
5 and 8, 7 and 42, 3 and 12, 1 and 1

Maths Investigation (p. 48)

PRIMES	2	3	5	7	11	13	17	19	23	29
SQUARE	1	4	9	16	25	36	49	64	81	100
TRIANGULAR	1	3	6	10	15	21	28	36	45	55
CUBES	1	8	27	64	125	216	343	512	729	1000

Can you think of three consecutive numbers that fit these categories:
Prime, cube, square? 7, 8, 9 // Square, triangular, prime? 9, 10, 11
Triangular, square, prime? 3, 4, 5 or 15, 16, 17

More Fun Factors (p. 50)
The factor pairs of 48 are: 1 and 48,
2 and 24, 3 and 16, 4 and 12, 6 and 8.

Top of the Class (p. 51)
Harry 45%, Ryan 85%, Mark 5%,
Logan 90%, Oliver 95%, Isla 60%,
Lily 70%, Heidi 100%, Emily 25%,
Freya 40%.

Murder in the Cathedral (p. 52)
29 / 12 / 1170

Mental Maths Ladder 2 (p. 53)
Ladder 1: 26, 2, 8, 24, 17, 6, 30, 3, 5
Final answer 35
Ladder 2: 10, 3, 9, 18, 54, 9, 18, 5, 20
Final answer 10
Ladder 3: 12, 60, 10, 120, 89, 49, 7, 17,
51 — Final answer 73
35, 10 and 73 = ELOISE

Deadly Decimals (p. 54)
See final table on page 64

A Mean Challenge (p. 55)
Below are some possible answers. These
lists are not exhaustive, so you may find a
solution that is not listed.
Four whole numbers which have a mean,
median, mode and range of four:
2, 4, 4, 6
Five whole numbers which have a mean,
median, mode and range of five:
3, 4, 5, 5, 8 // 2, 5, 5, 6, 7
Six whole numbers which have a mean,
median, mode and range of six:
3, 6, 6, 6, 6, 9 // 3, 4, 6, 6, 8, 9
2, 6, 6, 6, 8, 8 // 4, 4, 6, 6, 6, 10
3, 5, 6, 6, 7, 9

Eight whole numbers which have a mean,
median, mode and range of eight:
4, 8, 8, 8, 8, 8, 8, 12 // 5, 6, 8, 8, 8, 8, 8, 13
3, 8, 8, 8, 8, 8, 10, 11 // 8, 8, 8, 8, 3, 9, 9, 11
8, 8, 8, 8, 4, 4, 12, 12 // 8, 8, 8, 8, 9, 7, 4, 12
8, 8, 8, 8, 10, 6, 4, 12 // 8, 8, 8, 8, 11, 5, 4, 12
8, 8, 8, 8, 7, 11, 3, 11 …
Ten whole numbers which have a mean,
median, mode and range of ten:
10, 10, 10, 10, 10, 10, 10, 10, 5, 15
10, 10, 10, 10, 10, 10, 9, 11, 5, 15
10, 10, 10, 10, 10, 10, 8, 12, 5, 15
10, 10, 10, 10, 10, 10, 7, 13, 5, 15
10, 10, 10, 10, 10, 10, 6, 14, 5, 15
10, 10, 10, 10, 10, 10, 5, 15, 5, 15
… there are many more possible solutions!

Crack the Code (p. 56)

Before a test you must prepare. Here are my top tips: The emphasis should be on hard work. Do not go to bed too late. Eat lots of fruit and vegetables and cut down on pies. Check you have the right stationery. Self-belief, good intentions and training will help. In summary, it is better not to have to do the test all over again because you did too little too late. Stay calm, don't worry and…you will comfortably succeed with ease. After the exams, looking back, you will see for yourself how much the hard work paid off. Your friends might even say, 'Oh I envy you for you are a cut above the rest!'

Additional Algebra (p. 58)

Winter Warmer: 6 boys are wearing a hat without a scarf
The Bright Side of the Road: 9, 11, 13, 15, 17
Age-old Problem: Harry is 19
Party Time: Red £29, Purple £12, Blue £6, Yellow £20, Green £18. Total Cost: £85

Magic Multiplication (p. 24) and More Magic Multiplication (p. 44)

×	12	2	4	5	3	11	9	7	10	6	8	1
6	72	12	24	30	18	66	54	42	60	36	48	6
11	132	22	44	55	33	121	99	77	110	66	88	11
8	96	16	32	40	24	88	72	56	80	48	64	8
3	36	6	12	15	9	33	27	21	30	18	24	3
7	84	14	28	35	21	77	63	49	70	42	56	7
10	120	20	40	50	30	110	90	70	100	60	80	10
12	144	24	48	60	36	132	108	84	120	72	96	12
5	60	10	20	25	15	55	45	35	50	30	40	5
2	24	4	8	10	6	22	18	14	20	12	16	2
9	108	18	36	45	27	99	81	63	90	54	72	9
4	48	8	16	20	12	44	36	28	40	24	32	4
1	12	2	4	5	3	11	9	7	10	6	8	1

Deadly Decimals (p. 54)

×	1.2	0.2	0.4	0.5	0.3	1.5	0.9	0.7	0.1	0.6	0.8	1.0
6	7.2	1.2	2.4	3	1.8	9	5.4	4.2	0.6	3.6	4.8	6
11	13.2	2.2	4.4	5.5	3.3	16.5	9.9	7.7	1.1	6.6	8.8	11
8	9.6	1.6	3.2	4	2.4	12	7.2	5.6	0.8	4.8	6.4	8
3	3.6	0.6	1.2	1.5	0.9	4.5	2.7	2.1	0.3	1.8	2.4	3
7	8.4	1.4	2.8	3.5	2.1	10.5	6.3	4.9	0.7	4.2	5.6	7
10	12	2	4	5	3	15	9	7	1	6	8	10
12	14.4	2.4	4.8	6	3.6	18	10.8	8.4	1.2	7.2	9.6	12
5	6	1	2	2.5	1.5	7.5	4.5	3.5	0.5	3	4	5
2	2.4	0.4	0.8	1	0.6	3	1.8	1.4	0.2	1.2	1.6	2
9	10.8	1.8	3.6	4.5	2.7	13.5	8.1	6.3	0.9	5.4	7.2	9
4	4.8	0.8	1.6	2	1.2	6	3.6	2.8	0.4	2.4	3.2	4
1	1.2	0.2	0.4	0.5	0.3	1.5	0.9	0.7	0.1	0.6	0.8	1